D1628361

Bawdy British Folk Songs

Compiled and arranged by
TONY McCARTHY

WITH GUITAR CHORDS

WOLFE PUBLISHING LIMITED
10 EARLHAM STREET · LONDON WC2

Printed in Great Britain by The Stellar Press Hatfield Herts

CONTENTS

TONY McCARTHY sings traditional songs and his own material, written in the traditional idiom, and accompanies himself on guitar, banjo and Anglo-German concertina. For a number of years he was a 'Minstrel' at the Elizabethan Rooms at the Gore Hotel, Queensgate and sang in leading folk clubs throughout the British Isles. He is presently specialising in television journalism.

ISBN 7234 0492 5

INTRODUCTION

BAWDY SONG is an integral part of the British tradition. To some of the collectors who went out to find what they imagined to be the dying music of the peasantry, at the end of the last century, this was a matter of some horror. They were impressed by the beauty of the melodies but felt obliged to edit or suppress many of the words.

Since their published editions of traditional material became standard fare for schoolrooms and drawing-rooms, many of us have memories of 'folk song' as a tinkling thing, full of pretty phrases but with little relation to anything happening in the adult and workaday world.

However, folk music would not have survived as it did, nor have become a very powerful influence on young people's music-making today, if this was all it amounted to. Far from being thus limited it is, on the contrary, strongly imbued with the deepest emotions and desires of every one of us - and that involves the sexual impulse.

So a very large body of traditional song is based on sexual themes; these are treated in many different ways, and related to many forms of experience. In a rural community, the sexuality of beast, crop and man - the common interest in fertility - was very strong. So there is perhaps lacking in much of the material that prurience and evasion which characterises some attitudes to sex in the modern world. Then, in the very clearest sense, sexuality was an everyday fact of life.

The bulk of these songs is a clear celebration of the joys and occasional troubles of sex as one of the main sources of pleasure - and sometimes amusement - that is given to us. Traditional song derives from many sources, and serves many occasions; it can treat its subject with great delicacy or a degree of coarseness. Certainly some of the songs would not have been allowed into the parlour, though enjoying great popularity at the inn.

Yet there is a clear distinction, if not an exact line, between traditional bawdry and the more conscious attitudes of composed songs variously characterised by the wits of the eighteenth century, the music hall of the nineteenth and the Rugby club songsters of today. These have, of course, certain merits, and many songs, in variation, have moved into and out of these fields from the tradition. Generally the folk songs are more concerned with relationships, and these others with mechanics and grotesquerie.

Traditional song was not only, in itself, an important element in the life of rural society, but also a source of conventional wisdom. Better than a dozen covert talks on the birds and the bees is the tale of Lovely Joan. O Dear O is a moving statement on a subject few would openly discuss, but many may secretly worry about. Rocking the Cradle is perhaps the other side of the coin. There is a strong commonsense morality in many of the themes, at the very least a sense of 'fair do's' in The Butcher and the Chambermaid and Blow Away the Morning Dew.

Folk music represents a shared experience; some songs are newly made, or redesigned to fit new circumstances; others fall away. The greatest seem to go on forever. In the past, most songs were passed simply from one singer to another, in what is known as the 'oral tradition'. The work of itinerant ballad sellers who sold scraps of paper with a mixture of songs old and new printed on them is becoming increasingly recognised as an important factor in the spread of the songs, while the labours of the great collectors like Cecil Sharp again placed much material into new hands.

But it remains true that the most important part in the 'folk process' is that of the individual singer, refining stories to his own taste, forgetting words, decorating the melody, adding material if it suits him. The continuing life of so many old songs shows how little the essentials of relations between man and woman have changed. Apart from a couple of modern compositions, few of the songs in this book can be less than a hundred years old and many, in one form or another, can be traced back much further. As collected here, the traditional songs happen to be the versions that I sing; to the reader and - I trust - singer, they are yours to do with as you like, to suit your own style or mood.

TONY McCARTHY

8

ALL FOURS

As I was out walking one midsummer's morning
The fields and the meadows were pleasant and gay;
'Twas there I espied a most beautiful female
As she was a-tripping all on the highway.
　　'Twas there I espied a most beautiful female
　　As she was a-tripping all on the highway.

I stepped up to her and boldly said to her:
'Where are you going so early this morn?'
She says: 'Kind sir, I am going to Windsor,
That pleasant place wherein I was born.'

I said: 'Fair maid, and shall I go with you,
All for to keep you sweet company?'
She turned herself round, and smiling so sweetly
Said: 'Sir, you may do just as you please.'

We had not walked a mile together
Before acquainted, acquainted we came.
I said: 'Fair maid, pray sit down beside me
And I shall show you a sweet, pleasant game.'

She says: 'Kind sir, I'm not given to gaming
But yet I'm willing, I'm willing to learn.
But the game we shall play, it must be All Fours,
And I shall beat you three to your one.'

She cut the cards, it was my turn to deal them,
I dealt myself one trump, it was only poor Jack;
And she had the Ace and the Deuce for to follow,
And those were the very best cards in the pack.

She played her Ace and she stole my Jack from me
Which made her High, Low, Jack and the Game.
She said: 'Kind sir, I freely beat you
Unless you can play the game over again.'

I picked up my hat and I bid her Good Morning
Although she was High, Low, Jack and the Game.
She says: 'Kind sir, come this way tomorrow –
We'll play that game over and over again.'

THE AYLESBURY GIRL

As I was going to Ayles-bury, 'twas on a mar-ket day, There came a lit-tle Ayles-bury girl a-jog-ging on the way. Her bus-iness was to mar-ket with but-ter, cheese and whey. And we both jogged on to-geth-er, my boys, sing fol-the-lol idd-le-all-day, And we both jogged on to-geth-er, my boys, sing fol-the-lol-idd-le-all-day.

As I was going to Aylesbury, 'twas on a market day,
There came a little Aylesbury girl a-jogging on the way.
Her business was to market with butter, cheese and whey
And we both jogged on together, my boys,
      sing fol-the-lol-iddle-all-day.

As we jogged on together, boys, together side by side,
This pretty little Aylesbury girl, her garter came untied.
As we jogged on together, boys, I unto her did say:
'Your garter's come untied, my love,'
      sing fol-the-lol-iddle-all-day.

'Oh now you've been so venturesome, so venturesome and free,
Oh now you've been so venturesome, won't you tie it up for me?'
'Oh yes, oh yes, if you do come under yonder shady tree';
So we both jogged on together, boys,
      sing fol-the-lol-iddle-all-dee.

And when we got to yonder grove, the grass was growing high,
We both sat down together, boys, her garter for to tie;
Such tying of a garter the likes I never did see
And we both rolled on together, boys,
      sing fol-the-lol-iddle-all-dee.

'Oh now you've had your will of me, pray tell to me your name,
Likewise your occupation, from where and whence you came.'
'My name is Johnny Rover, from Dublin Town I came
And I live at the sign of the 'Ups and Downs'
      sing fol-the-lol-iddle-all-day.

And when she came to Aylesbury her butter was not sold
And losing of her maidenhead, it made her blood grow cold.
But now he's gone, so let him go, he's not the lad for me
For he lives at the sign of the 'Ups and Downs'
      sing fol-the-lol-iddle-all-dee.

BALL OF YARN

One sun-ny morn in May, as I was on my way To

vis - it my grand - fath - er's farm, I

spied a pret-ty maid a - rest-ing in the shade, She was

wind -ing up her lit -tle ball of yarn, ball of yarn, ball of

yarn She was wind-ing up her lit-tle ball of yarn. Oh the

black-bird and the thrush They sang out from every bush: 'Keep your

hands off her lit - tle ball of yarn!'

One sunny morn in May, as I was on my way
To visit my grandfather's farm,
I spied a pretty maid a-resting in the shade,
She was winding up her little ball of yarn.
> Ball of yarn, ball of yarn
> She was winding up her little ball of yarn.
> Oh the blackbird and the thrush
> They sang out from every bush:
> 'Keep your hands off her little ball of yarn.'

A pretty girl was May as she lay there in the hay,
The scene it was so quiet and so calm;
So I sat down where she lay and unto her did say:
'May I wind up your little ball of yarn?'

'No, kind sir,' says she, 'you're a stranger unto me
Though to other girls you may possess some charm;
You'd better go away and come back some other day
To wind up my little ball of yarn.'

But then I took my love down to some shady grove
And I never meant to do her any harm,
For the blackbird and the thrush they came out from every bush
To remind her of her little ball of yarn.

Ten months have passed and gone since I met my fair young one,
Then I met her with a baby on her arm;
But she didn't know 'twas me till I told her it was he
Who had wound up her little ball of yarn.

Now come all you young and old, take a warning when you're told
Never rise too early in the morn;
Be like the blackbird and the thrush, keep one hand on your bush
And the other on your little ball of yarn.

BILLY BOY

Where have you been all the day, Bill - y
Boy, Bill - y Boy, Where have you been all the day, my Bill-y
Boy? I've been court- ing all the day___ with my
char - ming Nan - cy Grey___ And my
Nan - cy tick- led my fan -cy, I'm her char-ming Bill- y Boy.

Where have you been all the day, Billy Boy, Billy Boy,
  Where have you been all the day, my Billy Boy?
I've been courting all the day with my charming Nancy Grey
  And my Nancy tickled my fancy, I'm her charming Billy Boy.

Can she cook and can she stew, Billy Boy, Billy Boy?
She can cook, she can stew, she can bake me oatcakes too.

Can she spin and can she sew, Billy Boy, Billy Boy?
She can spin, she can sew, lets me dig and helps me hoe.

Is she fitting to your wife, Billy Boy, Billy Boy?
She's as fitting to my wife as the haft is to the knife.

Did she light your way to bed, Billy Boy, Billy Boy?
She lit my way to bed with the nodding of her head.

Did she lie so close to you, Billy Boy, Billy Boy?
She lay as close to me as the bark does to the tree.

BLOW AWAY THE MORNING DEW

It's of a rich young farmer
Who lived out on the hill;
He went out one May morning
To see what he could kill.
      Singing: Blow away the morning dew,
             The dew and the dew.
             Blow away the morning dew,
             How sweet the winds do blow.

He looked up and he looked down,
He gave an under-look;
And what should he see but a fair pretty maid
A-swimming in the brook.

It's better for young ladies
To be sewing silken skeins,
Than to be out on a May morning
A-swimming against the stream.

It's better for young gentlemen
To be minding their business at home,
Than to be out on a May morning
A-watching young ladies swim.

'Do not touch my mantle
And leave my cloak alone,
But take me to my father's house
And carry me back home.'

So he put her upon one horse
And he rode on the other;
And there they rode along together
Like sister and like brother.

They rode along together
Till they came to some stooks of hay.
'O don't you think this a pretty place
For a boy and a girl to play?

'Take me to my father's house
And there you can lay me down;
And you shall have your will of me
And fifteen hundred pounds.'

But when she came to her father's gate
How quickly she ran in;
And none was more ready then her servant-maid
To rise and let her in.

And when she got inside her gate
She turned herself about.
She says: 'I am a maid within
And you're a fool without.

'There is a cock in father's yard
That never trod a hen,
Yet still he fluffs his feathers out
And I think you're one of them.

'There is a flower in mother's garden
Some do call it rue,
It causes all them pretty girls
To come and laugh at you.

'There is a flower in mother's garden
It's called marigold,
And if you would not when you might
You may not when you wolde.'

BLOW THE CANDLE OUT

The night that I enlisted, I went to see my dear,
The candles were all burning, the moon shone bright and clear;
I went to my love's window, and quickly she looked out,
Then rose to let me in, and then blew the candle out.

Saying: 'Willie, dearest Willie, tonight will be your doom,
Strip off into your nightshirt and come into my room;
The streets they are too lonely, love, for you to walk about,
So roll me in your arms, love, and blow the candle out.

'My father and my mother in yonder room do lie
A-hugging one another, so why not you and I?
A-hugging one another with never fear or doubt,
So roll me in your arms, love, and blow the candle out.'

It was six months later, six months ago today,
I wrote to her a letter when I was far away;
I wrote her a letter without fear or doubt
But never told her I'd be back to blow the candle out.

THE BUTCHER AND THE CHAMBERMAID

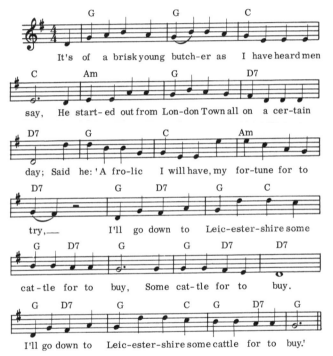

It's of a brisk young butcher as I have heard men say,
He started out from London Town all on a certain day;
Said he: 'A frolic I will have, my fortune for to try,
I'll go down to Leicestershire some cattle for to buy,
Some cattle for to buy.
I'll go down to Leicestershire some cattle for to buy.'

Now he arrived in Leicestershire and stopped at an inn,
He called for liquors of the best, his business to begin;
He called for liquors of the best and being a roving blade
He presently did fix his eye upon the chambermaid.

When the day was over, the night was coming on,
The butcher came back to his inn, his business being done;
He called for his supper, the reckoning left unpaid
Says he: 'This night I'll play a trick upon the chambermaid.'

So she then took a candle to light him up to bed,
And when they came into his room, these words to her he said:
'One sovereign I'll give to you all to enjoy your charms,'
So all night long this fair maid slept all in the butcher's arms.

He rose in the morning and prepared to go away;
The landlady said: 'Your reckoning, sir, you have forgot to pay.'
'Oh, no,' the butcher did reply, 'and do not think it strange,
One sovereign I gave your maid, but did not get the change.'

He straightway called the chambermaid and charged her with the same;
The sovereign she did lay down, for fear of getting blamed.
The butcher he went home, well pleased with what was past,
For very soon this chambermaid grew thicker round the waist.

Then in a twelve-months after, he came that way again,
And then as he had done before, he stopped at that inn;
And soon the buxom chambermaid chanced him to see,
And brought a babe just three months old and placed it on his knee.

The butcher sat like one amazed and at the child did stare,
And when the joke he did find out, how he did stamp and swear;
'Kind sir,' she said, 'it is your own, and do not think it strange,
One sovereign you did give me and I have brought you change.'

The company they laughed and smiled, the joke went freely round,
And the tidings of the same spread through Leicester Town;
The butcher was to a Justice brought who happened to live near,
One hundred pounds he did lay down before he could get clear.

So all you brisk young butchers, a warning take by me,
Look well into your bargain, before you money pay;
Or else perhaps your folly will give you cause to range –
For if you sport with chambermaids you're sure to get your change.

THE BUTCHER AND THE TAILOR'S WIFE

There was a wealthy tailor
In London Town did dwell,
He had a handsome wife
And her name was Mary Bell.
She's gone to market
A joint of meat to buy:
'What is your will, dear madam,'
The butcher did reply.

The joint of meat it was cut down,
Refuse it she did not;
Straightway she fetched it home
And put it in the pot.
And when the tailor had come home
She told him what she had,
And then the tailor leaped for joy,
His heart was very glad.

'Dear husband, dear husband,
I'll tell you how it must be,
Tomorrow night the butcher
He has to lie with me.
Take your broad sword in your hand
And under the bed go,
The first man that enters then
Be sure to run him through.'

'I never handled sword or gun,
My dear and loving wife;
The butchers they are bloody dogs
I'm afraid he'll have my life.'
'Do not be faint-hearted,
But with courage stout and bold;
And if the butcher you o'ercome,
You'll wear a chain of gold.'

The butcher thinking it was time
To see the tailor's wife,
And fearing they should form a plot
Or trick to take his life
He got a brace of pistols loaded
With powder and with ball.
'The first man that molests me now
By Jove, I'll make him fall.'

When the butcher he came in
She took him by the hand,
And led him to her bed chamber:
'Sir, I'm at your command.'
He pulled out his brace of pistols
And laid them on the bed;
The poor tailor was struck with fear
And lay as if quite dead.

As he was taking off his clothes
And going into bed,
How he was struck when he did spy
One of the tailor's legs.
'Is this your husband's dog?' he says,
'I'll shoot him for the fright.'
'O spare my life,' the tailor cries,
'And you shall have my wife!'

CRUISING ROUND YARMOUTH

While cruising round Yarmouth one day for a spree, I
met a fair dam-sel, the wind blow-ing free; 'I'm a
fast go-ing clip-per, my kind sir,' said she, 'I'm
rea-dy for car-go, my hold it is free.' Sing-ing:
Fal - the-ral - lad-dy right fal -the-ral - day,
Fal - the-ral lad-dy right fal - the-ral - day.

While cruising round Yarmouth one day for a spree,
I met a fair damsel, the wind blowing free;
'I'm a fast going clipper, my kind sir,' said she,
'I'm ready for cargo, my hold it is free.'
    Singing: Fal-the-ral-laddy right fal-the-ral-day,
              Fal-the-ral-laddy right fal-the-ral-day.

26

I gave her a rope and I took her in tow,
From yardarm to yardarm a-towing we go,
I lifted her hatches, found plenty of room,
And into her cabin I stuck my jib-boom.

She took me upstairs and her topsails she lowered,
In a neat little parlour she soon had me moored;
She laid in her foresails, her staysails and all,
Let her lily-white hand on my reef-tackle fall.

I said: 'Pretty fair maid, it's time to give o'er,
Betwixt wind and water you've run me ashore;
My shot locker's empty and powder's all spent,
I can't fire a shot, for it's choked at the vent.'

Here's luck to the girl with the black curly locks;
Here's luck to the girl who ran Jack on the rocks;
Here's luck to the doctor who eased all his pain;
He squared his mainyards, he's cruising again.

THE CUCKOO'S NEST

There is a thorn bush in oor kail-yard, There is a thorn bush in oor kail-yard, At the back of the thorn bush there stands a lad and lass, But they're bu-sy, bu-sy hair-in' at the cuck-oo's nest. It's hi the cuck-in, ho the cuck-in, hi the cuck-oo's nest, It's hi the cuck-in, ho the cuck-in, hi the cuckoo's nest. I'll gie an-y-one a shilling and a bot-tle o' the best, If they'll rum-ple up the fea-thers on the cuck-oo's nest.

28

There is a thorn bush in oor kail-yard,
There is a thorn bush in oor kail-yard,
At the back of the thorn bush there stands a lad and lass,
But they're busy, busy hairin' at the cuckoo's nest.
> It's hi the cuckin, ho the cuckin, hi the cuckoo's nest,
> It's hi the cuckin, ho the cuckin, hi the cuckoo's nest.
> I'll gie anyone a shilling and a bottle o' the best,
> If they'll rumple up the feathers on the cuckoo's nest.

It is thorned, it is sprinkled, it is compassed all around,
It is thorned, it is sprinkled and it isn't easy found;
She said: 'Young man, you're blundering,' I said it was nae true
And I left her with the makings o' a young cuckoo.

Some do like the lassies that's gay weel dressed,
And some like the lassies that's ticht aboot the waist;
But it's in among the blankets that I like best
To get a jolly rattle at the cuckoo's nest.

THE DERBY RAM

As I went out in Derby,
'Twas in the month of May,
I spied the biggest ram, me lads,
That ever fed on hay.

> And it's true, me lads,
> It's true, me lads,
> I've never been known to lie;
> If you'd have been in Derby
> You'd have seen it the same as I.

The wool on this ram's back, me lads,
It reached up to the moon;
A little boy went up in May,
And didn't come down till June.

This ram it had two horns, me lads,
And they were made of brass;
And one grew out of his head, me lads,
And the other grew out of his arse.

This ram it had great legs, me lads,
On them it did stand;
And every one of these great legs
It covered an acre of land.

The butcher that killed the ram, me lads,
Was drowned by the blood;
And the little boy that carried the bowl
Was washed away in the flood.

It took all the boys in Derby
To bear away his bones;
It took all the girls in Derby
To roll away his stones.

THE FIRE SHIP

As I set out one ev-en-ing, up-on a night's car-eer, I spied a lof-ty clip-per ship and to her I did steer; She hoist-ed up her sig-a-nals which I so quick-ly knew, And when she saw my bun-ting up she imm-ed-iate-ly hove to-oo-oo.___ She had a dark and a rov-ing eye-I-I, And her hair hung down in ring-a-lets; She was a nice girl, a de-cent girl, but one of the rak-ish kind.

As I set out one evening, upon a night's career,
I spied a lofty clipper ship and to her I did steer;
She hoisted up her sig-a-nals, which I so quickly knew,
And when she saw my bunting up she immediately hove to.
    She had a dark and a roving eye,
    And her hair hung down in ringalets;
    She was a nice girl, a decent girl,
    But one of the rakish kind.

Now, sir, won't you excuse of me for staying out so late,
And if my parents heard of this, then sad would be my fate;
My daddy, he's a minister, a good and righteous man,
My mother, she's a methodist, I do the best I can.

I took her to a tavern and I toasted her in wine,
Little did I think she was one of the rakish kind;
I handled her, I dandled her, and much to my surprise
It turns out she is a fire ship done up in a disguise.

So come all you bold sailor boys, that sails the wintry seas,
And come all you good whaler boys, a warning take by me;
Beware of lofty clipper ships, they'll be the ruin of you,
For she not only made me walk the plank, she set fire to
    me mainmast too!

THE FOGGY DEW

When I was young and in my prime I
foll-owed the rak-ish trade, And all the harm that
ev-er I done Was court-ing a fair young
maid; I court-ed her in the sum-mer-time, And
part of the win-ter too, And all the harm that
ever I done Was to keep off the fog-gy
dew, dew, dew, Was to keep off the fog-gy dew.

When I was young and in my prime
I followed the rakish trade,
And all the harm that ever I done
Was courting a fair young maid;
I courted her in the summertime,
And part of the winter too,
And all the harm that ever I done
Was to keep off the foggy dew, dew, dew,
Was to keep off the foggy dew.

One night as I lay in my bed,
Taking my farmer's sleep,
This pretty young girl came to my bedside
And bitterly did she weep;
She wept, she moaned, she tore her hair,
Crying, asking: 'What shall I do?
For tonight I've resolved to lie with you
For fear of the foggy dew, dew, dew,
For fear of the foggy dew.'

Now in the first part of that night
How we did sport and play,
And in the latter part of that night,
Close in my arms she lay;
And when the morning did appear
She asks: 'What have I done?'
O hush your noise, you foolish young girl,
For the foggy dew is gone, gone, gone,
The foggy dew is gone.

Now if that you should have one child,
It would make you laugh and smile,
And if that you should have another
It would make you think the while;
And if that you should have another,
Another and another one too,
It would make you leave off your foolish young tricks
And think on the foggy dew, dew, dew,
And think on the foggy dew.

I loved that girl with all my heart,
Sure as I loved my life,
But in the latter part of the year
She became another man's wife;
I never tell him of her faults,
Be damned if I ever do,
But every time she winks and smiles
I think on the foggy dew, dew, dew,
I think on the foggy dew.

THE FURZE FIELD

I have a furze field, my own dear-est jewel, Where
all my fine phea-sants do fly,_____ And if
you come a - shoot - ing while shoot-ing's in sea-son I'll
tell you, love, how to pro - ceed:_____ You
bring your dog with you, your gun in your hand, All
load - ed and primed, all at your com - mand; When the
phea-sants take flight, you must take sight, And
shoot the next mom-ent - you're sure to be right.

I have a furze field, my own dearest jewel,
Where all my fine pheasants do fly,
And if you come a-shooting while shooting's in season
I'll tell you, love, how to proceed:
You bring your dog with you, your gun in your hand,
All loaded and primed, all at your command;
When the pheasants take flight, you must take sight,
And shoot the next moment - you're sure to be right.

I have a fishpond, my own dearest jewel,
Where all my fine fishes do play,
If you come a-fishing while fishing's in season
I'll tell you, love, how to proceed:
You bring your nets with you, your rod in your hand,
Your hooks and your angles all at your command;
When you throw in, all the fishes will play,
It's down to the bottom - and that's the right way.

I have a warren, my own dearest jewel,
Where all my fine rabbits do play,
And if you come ferreting while ferreting's in season
I'll tell you, love, how to proceed:
You bring your dog with you, your ferret in your hand,
Your spade and your nets all at your command;
And the ferret will bolt, and the rabbits will play,
For it's down to the bottom - and that's the right way.

I have a deer park, my own dearest jewel,
Where all my fine deer I do keep,
And if you come a-hunting while hunting's in season
I'll tell you, love, how to proceed:
You bring your dog with you, your nag in your hand,
All saddled and bridled, all at your command;
The deer they will prowl, the dogs they will brawl,
It's then: Gee up Dobbin! - and back they will fall.

THE GENTLEMAN SOLDIER

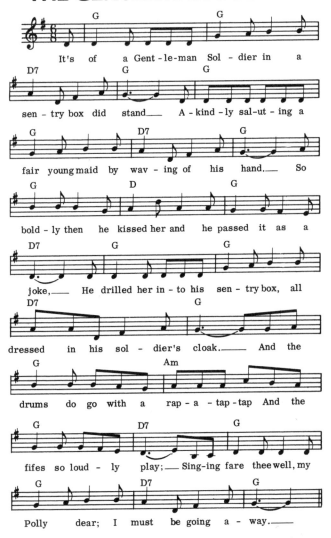

It's of a Gent-le-man Sol-dier in a sen-try box did stand___ A-kind-ly sal-ut-ing a fair young maid by wav-ing of his hand.___ So bold-ly then he kissed her and he passed it as a joke,___ He drilled her in-to his sen-try box, all dressed in his sol-dier's cloak.___ And the drums do go with a rap-a-tap-tap And the fifes so loud-ly play;___ Sing-ing fare thee well, my Polly dear; I must be going a-way.___

It's of a Gentleman Soldier in a sentry box did stand
A-kindly saluting a fair young maid by waving of his hand.
So boldly then he kissed her and he passed it as a joke,
He drilled her into his sentry box, all dressed in his soldier's cloak.
>   And the drums do go with a rap-a-tap-tap
>   And the fifes so loudly play;
>   Singing fare thee well, my Polly dear;
>   I must be going away.

There they tossed and tumbled till daylight did appear,
The soldier rose, put on his clothes, said:
>   'Fare thee well, my dear,
For I hear the bugles calling and I must be going away,
If it weren't for that, my Polly dear, I'd gladly with you stay.'

'Now, my Gentleman Soldier, won't you marry me?'
'No, my dearest Polly, such things can never be;
For I am married already and children I have three.
Two wives are allowed in the Army,
But one's too many for me.

'If anyone should ask you, say you're a country lass,
If anyone should ask you, give them a maidenly kiss;
You needn't ever tell them you ever played this joke
And spent the night in a sentry box, all wrapped in a soldier's cloak.'

'It's come, my Gentleman Soldier, why didn't you tell me so?
My parents will be angry when this they get to know,'
A few months they was up and passed,
>   the poor girl brought her shame –
She had a little militia-lad and didn't know his name.

GENTLY, JOHNNY MY JINGALO

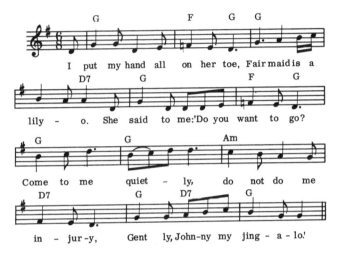

I put my hand all on her toe,
    Fair maid is a lily - o.
She said to me: 'Do you want to go?
    Come to me quietly, do not do me injury,
    Gently, Johnny my jingalo.'

I put my hand all on her calf.
She said to me: 'Don't do it by half.'

I put my hand all on her knee.
She said to me: 'Do you want to see?'

I put my hand all on her thigh.
She said to me: 'Do you want to try?'

I put my hand all on her belly.
She said to me: 'Do you want to fill'ee?'

I put my hand all on her head.
She says: 'You want my maidenhead.'

A GERMAN CLOCKWINDER

A German clockwinder to Dublin once came,
Benjamin Fooks was that blond German's name;
And as he was winding his way through the land
He played on his harp and his music was grand.
    With your tool-a-lumma, tool-a-lumma, toodle-aye-ay.

Oh there was a young lady from Grosvenor Square,
Who said that her clock was in need of repair;
In walks the blond German and to her delight
In less than five minutes he had put her right.

Now as they were seated down on the floor,
There came this very loud knock on the door;
In walked the husband and great was his shock
To find the blond German had wound his wife's clock.

The husband says he: 'Now look here, Mary Jane,
Don't let that blond German in here again;
He wound up your clock and left mine on the shelf –
If your old clock needs winding, I'll do it myself.'

THE GREY HAWK

Once I had a grey hawk, and a pret-ty grey hawk, A sweet pret-ty bird of my own;___ But she took her flight and she flew a-way quite___ And no-bod-y knows where she's gone, my brave boys, There's nobody knows where she's gone.___

Once I had a grey hawk, and a pretty grey hawk,
A sweet pretty girl of my own;
But she took her flight and she flew away quite
And nobody knows where she's gone, my brave boys,
There's nobody knows where she's gone.

It's over the mountains I've rambled away,
And through the green parks I have strayed;
I hollered, I whooped and I played on my flute
But no pretty bird could I find, my brave boys,
But no pretty bird could I find.

It's through the green forests I rambled away,
And through those green fields I did stray;
It's there I did spy my pretty grey hawk
Close wrapped in the arms of a man, my brave boys,
She was wrapped in the arms of a man.

Happy's the man that has a good wife,
Twice happier he that has none;
But cursed is he that courteth another's
While he has a good wife of his own, my brave boys,
While he has a good wife of his own.

Now he that has got her is welcome to her,
To do the best with her he can;
But whilst he has her, and I have her not
I'll hawk with her once now and then, my brave boys,
I'll hawk with her once now and then.

THE HANDSOME CABIN BOY

It's of a hand-some fe - male, as you may un-der-stand, Who had a mind to rove and go in - to some for-eign land; She dressed in sail-or's clo-thing, and to the coast did steer, And en - gag - ed with a cap - tain to serve him for one year.

It's of a handsome female, as you may understand,
Who had a mind to rove and go into some foreign land;
She dressed in sailor's clothing, and to the coast did steer,
And engaged with a captain to serve him for one year.

She engaged with the captain, a cabin boy to be,
The wind it being in favour, they soon put out to sea;
The captain's lady being on board, she seemed in great joy
To see her husband had engaged that handsome cabin boy.

So nimble was this pretty girl, she did her duty well,
But mark what follows after, the story I shall tell;
By eating captain's biscuits her colour did destroy,
And the waist did swell of pretty Nell, the handsome cabin boy.

As through the Bay of Biscay the gallant ship did plough,
One night amongst the sailors there was a pretty row;
They bundled from their hammocks, which did their rest destroy,
And they cursed about the groaning of the handsome cabin boy.

'O doctor, O doctor,' the cabin boy did cry,
The sailors swore by one and all the cabin boy should die;
The doctor ran with all his might, smiling at the fun,
To think a cabin boy should have a daughter or a son.

O when the sailors heard the joke, they all began to stare,
'This child belongs to none of us,' they solemnly declared;
'The lady to the captain said: 'Sir, I wish you joy,
It was either you or I betrayed the handsome cabin boy.'

So let's fill up a bumper and drink success to trade,
And likewise to the cabin boy that's neither man nor maid;
And if the wars should come again old England to destroy,
We shall ship some other sailors like the handsome cabin boy.

HOME, BOYS, HOME

I knew a ser-vant-maid, down in Dru - ry Lane, The mast - er he was good to her, the mis - tress was the same; Till one night a sail - or - lad___ chanced there for to stay, And that was the be - gin - ning of my true love and me. For it's home, boys, home, It's home I'd like to be; Home for a while in my own count - er - ee Where the oak, the

ash, and the bon-ny will-ow tree They all are grow-ing tall___ in my own coun-ter-ee.

I knew a servant-maid, down in Drury Lane,
The master he was good to her, the mistress was the same;
Till one night a sailor-lad chanced there for to stay,
And that was the beginning of my true love and me.

   For it's home, boys, home,
   It's home I'd like to be;
   Home for a while in my own counter-ee,
   Where the oak, the ash, and the bonny willow tree
   They all are growing tall in my own counter-ee.

I asked her for a candle to light my way to bed,
And likewise for a handkerchief to wrap around my head;
To wrap round my head as I used to do
And I said: 'My pretty Polly, won't you come to bed too?'

Early next morning, the sailor he arose,
And into her bosom throws handfuls of gold;
Saying: 'This I will give you, and more I shall do,
If you will be my true love wherever I go.

'Now if you had a daughter, call her after me,
And if you have a son you can send him off to sea
With his bell-bottomed trousers and jacket of true-blue,
And he will climb the rigging like his daddy used to do.'

I AM A COACHMAN

I am a coachman all on the high road,
Kissing and courting are all in my mode;
I kiss them, I court them, I lay by their side,
And when I get tired away I do ride.
        Derry down, down, down derry down.

I am a jockey, I ride a fine mare,
I always go straight, and I always go fair;
I keep on a-trying, I never give in,
I'm up in my stirrups until I do win.

I am a ploughman, I plough a good furrow,
In the good soft earth my plough it does burrow;
I keep on a-ploughing from daybreak till dusk,
And my plough is shiny, it never shows rust.

I am a postman, I call every day,
I bring her the post when her husband's away;
She gets so excited whenever I knock
And pushes my letters into her box.

I'm a lamplighter, I keep my wick trimmed,
And I'm much on call when the winter draws in;
I go down the streets before five o'clock
And the ladies light up at the sound of my knock.

JOHN ANDERSON, MY JO

John Anderson, my jo John, I wonder what ye mean
To lie sae lang i' the morning and sit sae late at e'en?
Ye'll blear a' your een, John, and why do ye so?
Come sooner to your bed at e'en, John Anderson, my jo.

John Anderson, my jo John, when that ye first began
Ye had as good a tail-tree as any other man.
But now it's waxin' wan, John, and wrinkles to and fro
And aft requires my helping hand, John Anderson, my jo.

When we were young and yauld, John, we've lain-out owre the dyke
And oh! it was fine thing to see your hurdies fyke.
To see your hurdies fyke, John, and strike the rising blow
'Twas then I liked your chanter-pipe, John Anderson, my jo.

John Anderson, my jo John, you're welcome when you please,
It's either in the warm-bed or else aboon the claes.
Do your part aboon, John, and trust to me below,
I've twa gae-ups for your gae-down, John Anderson, my jo.

When ye come on before, John, see that ye do your best,
When I begin to haud ye, see that ye grip me fast.
See that ye grip me fast, John, until that I cry: 'Oh!'
Your back shall crack, or I do that, John Anderson, my jo.

I'm backit like a salmon and breastit like a swan,
My wyme is like a down-cod, my waist ye weel may span.
My skin fra tap to tae, John, is like the new fa'n snow,
And it's all for your conveniency, John Anderson, my jo.

(Lyric: Robert Burns, adapted from traditional material)

THE JOLLY TINKER

I am a jolly tinker, at a door I chanced to knock
And said: 'Have you any kettles or some rusty holes to block?'
Well indeed I have, don't you know I have,
With me rifle-oor-a-laddy, don't you know I have?

She brought me through the kitchen and she brought me through the hall,
And the servants cried: 'The Devil! Has he come to block us all?'
     Well, indeed I've not.

She brought me up the stairs to show me what to do,
And she fell on the feather bed, and I fell on it too.
     Well indeed I did.

She took up the frying pan and she began to knock
To tell the servants down below that I was at my work.
     Well indeed I was.

She put her hand in her pocket and pulled out fifty pound
And said: 'My jolly tinker, we shall have another round.'
     Well indeed I will.

She put her hand in her pocket and pulled out a gold watch,
Saying: 'Take this, my jolly tinker, for I know you are no botch.'
     Well indeed I'm not.

Now I've been a jolly tinker man for fifty years or more
But a rustier old hole than that, I've never blocked before.
     Well indeed I haven't.

THE KEACH IN THE CREEL

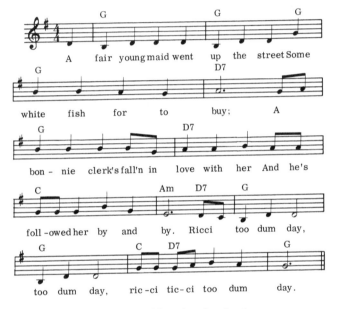

A fair young maid went up the street
Some white fish for to buy;
A bonnie clerk's fall'n in love with her
And he's followed her by and by.
    Ricci too dum day, too dum day,
    Ricci ticci too dum day.

'O where are you going, my bonnie lass,
I pray thee tell to me;
O if the night be never so dark,
I'll come and visit thee.'

'My father locks the door at even,
My mother keeps the key;
If you were never such a roving blade,
You'd never win-in to me.'

But the clerk he had a young brother,
And a wily wag was he;
He's made him a long ladder,
With thirty steps and three.

And he's put it to the chimney top,
And the creel he's put on a pin;
And he's tied it to the chimney top,
And let the young clerk in.

The old wife she was standing by,
She heard a word was said;
'I could lay my life,' says the silly old wife,
'There's a man in our daughter's bed.'

The old man he got out of bed,
To see if the thing were true;
But she's taken the bonny clerk in her arms
And covered him o'er with blue.

'O where are you going now, father,' she says,
'And where are you going so late?
You've disturbed me in my evening prayers
and O, but they were sweet.'

'O ill betide you, silly old wife,
And an ill death may you die;
She has the good book in her arms,
And she's praying for you and I.'

The old wife being not asleep,
The something more was said;
'I'll lay my life,' said the silly old wife,
'There's a man in our daughter's bed.'

'O get up yourself,' the old man said,
'The Devil may have you fast;
Between your daughter and yourself
I cannot get my night's rest.'

Up then got the old goodwife,
To see if it were true -
And she fell arselins in the creel
And up the string they drew.

'Wake up, wake up, good man!' she cries,
'Wake up and help me now.
For he that you gave me to last night,
I think he's caught me now!'

'If that foul thief's gotten you,
May he hold you tight;
For you'll never stay in your bed,
Nor rest with me at night.'

He's towed her up, he's towed her down
And given her a right down-fall;
Till every rib on the old wife's side
Played nick-nack on the wall.

O the blue, the bonnie, bonnie blue,
And I wish it may do well -
And every old wife that's jealous of her daughter
Get a good keach in the creel.

THE KEEPER

The Keeper did a-hunting go,
Under his arm he carried a bow,
All for to shoot at a merry little doe
Among the leaves so green-o.
> Jackie Boy - Master?
> Sing ye well? - Very well.
> Hey down, ho down,
> Derry, derry down
> Among the leaves so green-o.

The first doe he shot at he missed,
The second doe he trimmed and kissed,
The third ran away where nobody wist
Among the leaves so green-o.

The next doe she did cross the brook,
The Keeper fetched her back with his long-hook,
What he done to her you can go and look
Among the leaves so green-o.

The next doe she did cross the hollow,
And where she went he soon did follow,
What he done today, he will do again tomorrow
Among the leaves so green-o.

The fourth doe she did cross the plain,
The Keeper fetched her back again,
He tickled her in a very merry vein
Among the leaves so green-o.

The last doe was a fallow doe,
As great with young as she could go,
She looked so big that he had to let her go
Among the leaves so green-o.

THE KETTLE SMOCK

A-striving and a-toiling as I was one day,
The thought of my true love, it led me astray;
But the day it being over, and the night a-coming on,
Away I did run with my kettle smock on.

I went to my love's window and cried: 'Are you in bed?'
She was lying there so quiet and lifted up her head;
She lifted up her head and she says: 'Is that John?'
'Yes indeed it is me with my kettle smock on.'

She opened up the window, and let me in
Saying: 'Sit down by the fireside and warm up your skin.'
Now the bedroom door was open, and the blankets all turned down
So I rolled her in my arms with my kettle smock on.

We tumbled and we tasted till the break of day
Not thinking on the hours that we did pass away;
Till my love she jumps up and she cries: 'What have I done?
For a baby will come with his kettle smock on.'

Now I chastised my love for talking so wild;
'My pretty little fair young thing, we'll never have a child,
For all that we've done it was only in fun' –
But away I did run, with my kettle smock on.

THE LARK IN THE MORN

The lark in the morning she do rise from her nest
And sings in the air with the dew all on her breast;
And with the pretty ploughboy she'll whistle and she'll sing
And at night she'll return to her nest once again.

As I was a-walking one morning in Spring
I heard a young damsel, so sweetly she did sing;
As we were a-walking, I heard the damsel say:
'There's no life like the ploughboy's in the merry month of May.'

Now when the ploughboy he has done all that he has to do
Perhaps to the country wake a-walking he will go;
And there with pretty Nancy he'll whistle and he'll sing
And at night he'll return to his home once again.

And when he is returning from the wake to the town
The grass it being mown and the hay it all cut down;
'If we should chance to tumble all in the new mown hay,
O kiss me now or never,' this pretty girl do say.

When twenty long weeks they were over and were passed
This pretty young girl she grew thick around the waist;
'It was the pretty ploughboy,'the damsel she did say,
'That caused me to tumble all in the new mown hay.

'Twas down in the meadow and in that private Park
Where he kissed me sweetly and gained my heart;
With his kisses so sweet and his humour so free
In spite of my own heart which made me agree.'

So good luck to the ploughboy wherever he may be
That likes to take a pretty girl to dandle on his knee;
With his bottle of strong ale, he'll whistle and he'll sing
And the ploughboy is as happy as a prince or a king.

THE LIMERICK RAKE

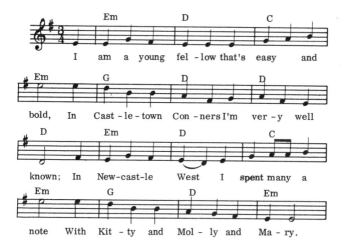

I am a young fellow that's easy and bold,
In Castletown Conners I'm very well known;
In Newcastle West I spent many a note
With Kitty and Molly and Mary.
My parents rebuked me for being such a rake
And spending my time in such frolicsome ways,
But I ne'er could forget the good nature of Jane,
Agus fagaimid siud mar ata se.

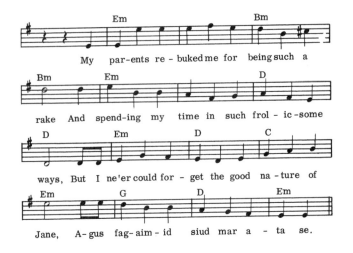

My parents they reared me to shake and to sow,
To plough and to harrow, to reap and to mow;
But my heart was too airy to drop it so low,
I set out on a high speculation.
On paper and parchment they taught me to write
And in Euclid and grammar they opened my eyes,
But in multiplication, in truth, I was bright,
Agus fagaimid siud mar ata se.

To quarrel for riches I ne'er was inclined,
For the greatest of misers must leave them behind;
I'll purchase a cow that will never run dry
And I'll milk her by twisting her horn.
John Damer of Shronel had plenty of gold
And Devonshire's treasure was twenty times more,
But he's laid on his back among nettles and stones,
Agus fagaimid siud mar ata se.

If I chance for to go to the market at Croom,
With a cock in my hat and my pipes in full tune,
I am welcome at once and brought up to a room
Where Bacchus is sporting with Venus.

There's Peggy and Jane from the town of Bruree,
And Biddy from Bruff and we all on the spree,
Such a combing of locks as there was about me,
Agus fagaimid siud mar ata se.

There's some say I'm foolish, there's more say I'm wise,
For love of the women I'm sure 'tis no crime;
For the son of King David had ten hundred wives
And his wisdom is highly recorded.
I'll till a good garden and live at my ease
And the women and children can partake of the same,
If there's war in the cabin, themselves are to blame,
Agus fagaimid siud mar ata se.

And now for the future I mean to be wise,
And I'll send for the women that treated me kind;
And I'll marry them all on the morrow, by and by
If the clergy agree to the bargain.
And when I'm on my back and my soul is at peace
The women will crowd for to cry at my wake,
And their sons and their daughters will utter their prayers
To the Lord for the sake of their father.

LONG PEGGIN' AWL

As I was— a – walk - ing one morn - ing— in May I— met a pret-ty fair maid, her gown it was gay; I step - ped up to her and back she did fall, She wants to be played with my long pegg - in' awl.

(Sung unaccompanied - freely)

As I was a-walking one morning in May
I met a pretty fair maid, her gown it was gay;
I stepped up to her and back she did fall,
She wants to be played with my long peggin' awl.

I said: 'Pretty fair maid, will you travel with me
Unto foreign countries strange things for to see?
And I will protect you, whate'er may befall
And follow your love with his long peggin' awl.'

Then home to her parents she went straight away
And unto her mother these words she did say:
'I'll follow my true love, whate'er may befall,
I'll follow my love with his long peggin' awl.'

'O daughter, O daughter, how can you say so?
For young men are false, you very well know;
They'll tell you fine things and the devil and all,
And leave you big-bellied with the long peggin' awl.'

'O mother, O mother, now do not say so.
Before you were sixteen you very well know
There was father and mother and baby and all -
You followed my dad for his long peggin' awl.'

LOVELY JOAN

A fine young man it was indeed
Came riding on his milk-white steed;
He rode, he rode and himself all alone
Until he came to lovely Joan.

'Good morning to you, my fair pretty maid.'
'And twice good morning to you, sir,' she said;
She smiled at him, he winked his eye,
Says he to himself, I'll be there by and by.

'Now don't you think these stooks of hay
A pretty place for us to play?
And come with me like a sweet young thing,
And I'll give you a golden ring.'

'Now give me this ring into my hand
And I shall neither stay nor stand;
This ring would be more use to me
Than fifty maidenheads,' said she.

But as he made for the stooks of hay
She leapt on his horse and she rode away;
He cursed, he swore, it was all in vain –
Young Joan she never looked back again.

She didn't think herself quite safe
Until she'd come to her own true-love's gate;
She'd robbed this young man of his golden ring
And left him to rage in the meadows green.

THE MAIDS OF AUSTRALIA

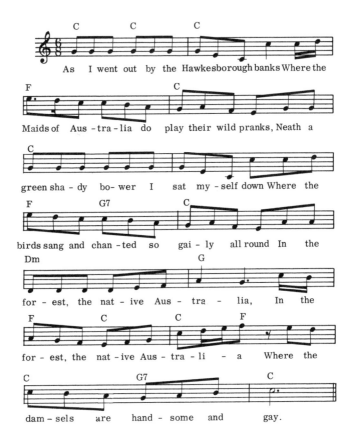

As I went out by the Hawkesborough banks Where the
Maids of Aus-tra-lia do play their wild pranks, Neath a
green sha-dy bo-wer I sat my-self down Where the
birds sang and chan-ted so gai-ly all round In the
for-est, the nat-ive Aus-tra-lia, In the
for-est, the nat-ive Aus-tra-li-a Where the
dam-sels are hand-some and gay.

As I went out by the Hawkesborough banks
Where the Maids of Australia do play their wild pranks,
Neath a green shady bower I sat myself down
Where the birds sang and chanted so gaily all round
     In the forest, the native Australia,
     In the forest, the native Australia
     Where the damsels are handsome and gay.

She jumped in the water without fear or dread
And her beautiful limbs she exceedingly spread;
Her hair hung in ringlets, its colour was black
'Sir,' says she, 'You can see how I float on my back,'
     In the forest, the native Australia,
     In the forest, the native Australia
     Where the damsels are handsome and gay.

She being exhausted, she swum to the brink
Crying: 'Help me, kind sir, or I surely shall sink!'
I quickly came to her and stretched out my hand,
And my foot slipped and we fell on the sand
     And I entered the bush of Australia
     And I entered the bush of Australia
     Where the damsels are handsome and gay.

There we did play with the greatest of ease
In the finest Australia you ever did see;
The sun it came up and the sun it went down
And I said, 'My fair maid, I must leave for the town,'
     And I left the bush of Australia
     And I left the bush of Australia
     Where the damsels are handsome and gay.

Nine long months being over and done
This beautiful girl she brought forth a fine son;
But where was the father? He couldn't be found
And she cursed the day that she lay on the ground
     In the bush of her native Australia
     In the bush of her native Australia
     Where the damsels are handsome and gay.

MAIDS WHEN YOU'RE YOUNG

An old man came court-ing me, Hey ding door-um down; An old man came court-ing me, Me be-ing young; An old man came court-ing me, Fain would he mar-ry me; Maids when you're young nev-er wed an old man. For he's got no fal-oor-um, fal-idd-le fal-oor-um, He's got no fal-oor-um, fal-idd-le fal-ay; He's got no fal-oor-um, he's lost his ding-door-um, (so) Maids when you're young ne-ver wed an old man.

An old man came courting me,
 Hey ding doorum down;
An old man came courting me,
 Me being young;
An old man came courting me,
Fain would he marry me;
Maids when you're young never wed an old man.
  For he's got no faloorum, fal-iddle faloorum,
  He's got no faloorum, fal-iddle fal-ay;
  He's got no faloorum, he's lost his ding-doorum,
  Maids when you're young never wed an old man.

When he came to court
When he came to court
When he came to court
I found him far too short;
Maids when you're young never wed an old man.

When we came to bed
When we came to bed
When we came to bed
He lay as he were dead;
Maids when you're young never wed an old man.

When that he went to sleep
When that he went to sleep
When that he went to sleep
Out of bed she did creep
Into the arms of a waiting young man.
  And she's found his faloorum, fal-iddle faloorum,
  She's found his faloorum, fal-iddle fal-ay;
  She's found his faloorum, he's got her ding-doorum,
  Maids when you're young never wed an old man.

THE MILLER AND THE LASS

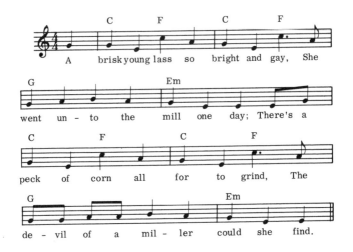

A brisk young lass so bright and gay, She
went un- to the mill one day; There's a
peck of corn all for to grind, The
de - vil of a mil - ler could she find.

A brisk young lass so bright and gay,
She went unto the mill one day;
There's a peck of corn all for to grind,
The devil of a miller could she find.

But then the miller did come in,
And this fair maid she did begin:
'There's a peck of corn all for the grind,
I can but stay a little time.'

'Come sit you down, my sweet pretty dear,
I cannot grind your corn, I fear;
My stones is high and my water low,
I cannot grind, for the mill won't go.'

Then she sat down all on a stack,
They talked of this, they talked of that;
They talked of love, of love proved kind,
She soon found out that mill would grind.

Then he got up the mill to grind,
And left her down the stones to mind;
Then an easy up and an easy down,
She scarce could tell when her corn was ground.

Then go you home, my sweet pretty dear,
The corn is ground and the mill is clear;
She swore she'd been ground by a score or more,
But never been ground so well before.

MOVING ON

See an old leave train coming down the track,
An Aussie on the front and a Yankee on the back: I'm
moving on; I'll soon be gone; I'd
like to stay, but the M P's say Keep Moving On.

See an old leave train coming down the track,
An Aussie on the front and a Yankee on the back:
    I'm moving on;
    I'll soon be gone;
    I'd like to stay, but the MPs say
    Keep Moving On.

I had a girl down in Seoul,
She kept treating my like a fool:

If I heard that bastard Syngman Rhee
Say one word of thanks to me:

I got a letter from my home
Said my old girl's got another man:
She's moving on.

I had a girl and she was willing
Now I'm taking penicillin:

Sexy, sexy, stick or bust,
If the Yanks don't get you, the women must:
      I'm moving on;
      I'll soon be gone;
      I'd like to stay, but the MPs say
      Keep Moving On.

THE NIGHTINGALES SING

As___ I was a – walk - ing one morn - ing in May I___ saw a fond coup - le a – mak - ing their way; And___ one was a fair__ maid, a beau-ty I de - clare, And the oth - er was a sol - dier, a bold gren - ad - ier. And they kissed so sweet and com-fort -ing as they clung to each oth - er,___ They went arm - ing a – long the road Like sis - ter and

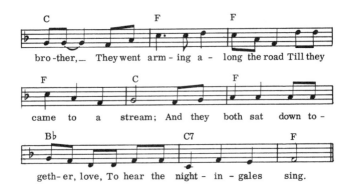

bro -ther,— They went arm - ing a - long the road Till they came to a stream; And they both sat down to - geth- er, love, To hear the night - in - gales sing.

As I was a-walking one morning in May
I saw a fond couple a-making their way;
And one was a fair maid, a beauty I declare,
And the other was a soldier, a bold grenadier.
 And they kissed so sweet and comforting
 As they clung to each other,
 They went arming along the road
 Like sister and brother,
 They went arming along the road
 Till they came to a stream;
 And they both sat down together, love,
 To hear the nightingales sing.

Then out of his knapsack he drew a fine fiddle
And he played her such merry tunes as she ever did hear;
He played her such merry tunes, caused the valleys to ring
'Hark hark,' says the fair maid, 'hear the nightingales sing.'

'Oh, come,' says the soldier, 'it's time to give o'er,'
'Oh no,' says the fair maid, 'let's play one tune more;
I do like to hear you play so well, and the touch of your string,
And to see the pretty flowers grow, hear the nightingales sing.

'Oh now,' says the fair maid, 'will you marry me?'
'Oh no,' says the soldier, ' how can that thing be?
For I have a wife at home in my own counteree,
And she's the sweetest little thing that you ever did see.'

THE NUTTING GIRL

Come all you jovial fellows, come listen to my song,
It is a little ditty and it won't detain you long;
It's of a fair young damsel and she lived down in Kent,
Arose one summer's morning and she a-nutting went.
> With me fal-lal to me ral-tal-lal
> Sing whack fol the dear-ol-day;
> And what few nuts that poor girl had
> She threw them all away.

And it's of a brisk young farmer was ploughing of his land,
He called unto his horses to bid them gently stand;
As he sat down all on his plough all for a song to sing,
His voice was so melodious, it made the valleys ring.

It's of this fair young damsel, she was nutting in a wood,
His voice was so melodious it charmed her as she stood;
His voice was so melodious, she could no longer stay,
And what few nuts that poor girl had, she threw them all away.

She then came to young Johnny as he sat on his plough,
She said: 'Young man, I really feel I cannot tell you how';
He took her to some shady broom and there he laid her down;
She said: 'Young man, I think I feel the world go round and round.'

Now come all you young women, this warning take from me,
If you should a-nutting go, please get home for tea;
For if you should stay too late to hear the ploughboy sing
You might have a young farmer to nurse up in the spring.

O DEAR O

As I was walking one midsummer's morning
To view the fields and leaves a-springing,
I saw two maidens standing by
And one of them her hands was wringing:
     O dear O, O dear O,
     My husband's got no courage in him,
     O dear O.

All sorts of meat I did provide,
All sorts of drink are fitting for him;
And oyster pie and rhubarb too,
But nothing would put courage in him.

My husband's admired wherever we go,
And every one looks well upon him;
By his hands and feet and well-shaped eye,
But still he's got no courage in him.

Seven long years I made his bed,
Six of them I lay beside him;
And this morning I arose with my maidenhead,
For still he had no courage in him.

I wish the Lord that he were dead,
And in his grave I'd quickly lay him;
Then I'd try another one,
That had a little courage in him.

Come all pretty maidens, wherever you be,
Don't marry a man before you try him;
Lest you should sing a song with me,
My husband's got no courage in him.

OH NO, JOHN, NO

On yonder hill there stands a creature,
Who she is I do not know;
I'll go and court her for her beauty,
She must tell me yes or no.
      Oh no, John, no John, no John, no.

My husband, he's a Spanish captain,
Went to sea a month ago;
First he kissed me, then he blessed me,
Bid me always answer, no.

Madam, in your eye is beauty,
In your bosom sweet flowers grow;
If I should chance to touch that posy,
Would you tell me yes or no?

Madam, shall I tie your garter,
Tie it a little above your knee;
If my hand should slip a little farther,
Would you think it amiss of me?

So my love and I went to bed together,
Lay there till the cock did crow;
Unclasp your arms, my dearest jewel,
Unclasp you arms, and let me go.
     Oh no, John, no John, no John, no.

PEGGY-O

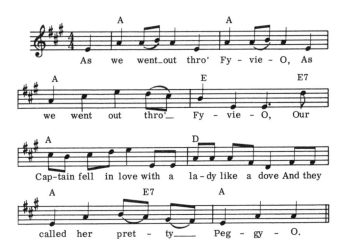

As we went out thro' Fy - vie - O, As
we went out thro'— Fy - vie - O, Our
Cap-tain fell in love with a la-dy like a dove And they
called her pret - ty— Peg - gy - O.

As we went out thro' Fyvie-O,
As we went out thro' Fyvie-O,
Our Captain fell in love with a lady like a dove
And they called her pretty Peggy-O.

Come tripping down the stair, pretty Peggy, my dear,
Come tripping down the stair, pretty Peggy-O,
Come tripping down the stair combing back your golden hair
And wave farewell to the Captain-O.

What would your mother think, pretty Peggy, my dear,
What would your mother think, pretty Peggy-O?
What would your mother think to hear the guineas clink
And see the soldiers marching before you-O.

Before we had come to old Meldrum Town
The Captain we had to carry-O;
And before we had come to the bonny braes of Doon
The Captain we had to bury-O.

If ever I return, pretty Peggy, my dear,
If ever I return, pretty Peggy-O,
If ever I return your fair city I shall burn
And destroy all the ladies of the aree-O.

O green grow the birks of old Aberdeen,
And low are the lowlands of Fyvie-O,
Our Captain fell in love and he died for a maid
And they called her pretty Peggy-O.

PUMP AWAY

I gave her presents one, presents one,
      Presents one,
I gave her presents one, presents one,
      Presents one,
I gave her presents one
And my story has begun.
      Put your shoulder next to mine and pump away,
      Pump away.
      Put your shoulder next to mine and pump away.

I gave her presents two
I gave her presents two
I gave her presents two
And my hand was on her shoe.

I gave her presents three
I gave her presents three
I gave her presents three
And my hand was on her knee.

I gave her presents four
I gave her presents four
I gave her presents four
And I rolled her on the floor.

I gave her presents five
I gave her presents five
I gave her presents five
She was glad she was alive.

I gave her presents six
I gave her presents six
I gave her presents six
And I taught her all my tricks.

I gave her presents seven
I gave her presents seven
I gave her presents seven
And she thought she was in heaven.

I gave her presents eight
I gave her presents eight
I gave her presents eight
And the doctor's at the gate.

I gave her presents nine
I gave her presents nine
I gave her presents nine
And the baby's doing fine.

I gave her presents ten
I gave her presents ten
I gave her presents ten
And she's started off again.

QUEER BUNGAREYE

As I was a-walking down Paradise Street,
To me way-ay blow the man down,
A pretty young doxy I chanced for to meet,
O give me some time to blow the man down.

'Now what's in your basket? 'so boldly says I;
Says she: 'Young Jack Tar, it's some queer bungareye.'

'Bungareye,' says I, 'now what can that be?'
'It's the finest old brandy, brought from Germany.'

So I gave her a guinea, she went for some change;
She'd been gone an hour, I thought it was strange.

I looked in the basket, and what did I see?
It wasn't good brandy, 'twas a little baby.

So off to the parson, the parson I went
To get the babe christened, it was my intent.

'Now what shall I call it?' asks the parson. Says I:
'The name you shall give it is Queer Bungareye.'

'Bungareye,' says the parson, 'that's a very strange name.'
'Bedamn me,' says I, 'it's a strange way he came.'

So come all you sailors, take warning by me
And never go drinking that German brandy.

RAP-A-TAP

My mas - ter went___ to mar - ket all for to sell his corn, Left me to mind his bus - i-ness just as he were__ at home; As soon as the mas-ter's back was turned, I bun-dled out of the barn And went to the door with a (rap - a - tap - tap) I'm sure I meant no harm,_ my boys, I'm sure I meant no harm.___

My master went to market all for to sell his corn,
Left me to mind his business just as he were at home;
As soon as the master's back was turned, I bundled out of the barn
And went to the door with a rap-a-tap-tap!
I'm sure I meant no harm, my boys,
I'm sure I meant no harm.

Soon as my missus heard me she quickly let me in,
She asked me if I was dry, my boys, she brought to me some gin;
And I was to drink it up, my boys, and never a word was to be said
That I'd been there with a rap-a-tap-tap!
Straightway we went to bed, my boys,
Straightway we went to bed.

We hadn't been in bed but half an hour or more,
She played to me such a pretty tune, I thought she'd never give o'er;
Saying: 'You've won my heart for ever, your master's no man for me,
He can't come with a rap-a-tap-tap!
Not half as well as thee,' my boys,
Not half as well as thee.

So my master came from market and asked me what I'd done,
I told him I'd minded his business as if he'd been at home;
So he ordered me some beer, my boys, but little did he know
That I'd been there with my rap-a-tap-tap!
Or else he'd never done so, my boys,
Or else he'd never done so.

So come all you jolly fellows wherever you may be,
That has a handy servantman, so handy and so free;
Before you leave your wife alone, and you do close the door
Give her so much of that rap-a-tap-tap!
She'll never want any more, my boys,
She'll never want any more.

THE RIGS OF LONDON TOWN

From London Town I went astray,
'Twas in Oxford City I lost my way;
The finest girl that I did meet,
She treated me with kisses sweet.
    I'm up to the rigs, down to the jigs,
    Up to the rigs of London Town.

She took me to some house of fame,
The Sign of the Ship in Water Lane;
A roaring supper she did call,
Thinking I should pay for all.

Now supper was over and the table clear,
She calls me her jolly and roving dear;
She calls for wine both white and red
And a chambermaid to make our bed.

Now between the hour of one and two
She asked me if to bed I'd go;
And I therewith I gave consent
And up to the bedroom door I went.

When this fair maid got fast asleep
Slowly from her I did creep;
I stole her watch, her silken gown,
Her gold rings and twenty pounds.

Now come all you young men, wherever you be,
When you meet with a lass that is jolly and free
Use her well, I done the same -
But remember the Ship in Water Lane.

ROCKING THE CRADLE

As I was a-walking one fine summer's morning,
Down by a clear river I walked all alone;
I heard a poor man making sad lamentation,
And thus he began to make his sad moan:

    O sweet baby lie easy,
    Your own daddy will never be known;
    It's weeping and wailing and rocking the cradle
    All over a baby that's none of my own.

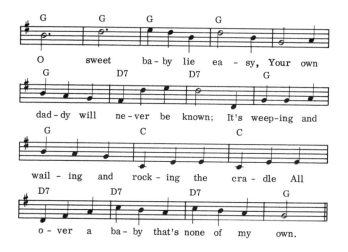

O sweet ba-by lie ea-sy, Your own
dad-dy will ne-ver be known; It's weep-ing and
wail-ing and rock-ing the cra-dle All
o-ver a ba-by that's none of my own.

When I first met with your innocent mother
I thought like a fool I was blessed with a wife;
Now to my sorrow, sad grief and vexation
She has proved a torture and plague to my life.

It's every day that she walks with her bully
And leaves me the cradle to rock all alone;
This innocent baby he calls me his daddy,
It's little he knows that he's none of my own.

My wife she comes in at the heel of the evening,
She calls to me smartly the kettle put down;
She sits to her table and to her tea-drinking,
She cries: 'You old cuckold, come rock the child sound.'

Now for to finish my sad lamentation,
All you that is single pray ne'er take a wife;
For if you do they will sorely torment you,
And prove a sad ruin all the days of your life.

ROLLING IN THE DEW

Where are you a-going to, my pretty fair maid?
    With your red rosy cheeks and your bright golden hair.
'I'm going a-milking, kind sir,' she answered me.
    'It's rolling in the dew makes the milkmaids fair.'

Shall I carry your pail for you, my pretty fair maid?
'No, I'll carry it myself, kind sir,' she answered me.

Suppose I was to kiss you, my pretty fair maid?
'There would be no harm there, kind sir,' she answered me.

Suppose I was to lay you down, my pretty fair maid?
'You must help me up again, kind sir,' she answered me.

Suppose that you have a child, my pretty fair maid?
'Then surely you would father it, kind sir,' she answered me.

Suppose that I should run away, my pretty fair maid?
'Then surely I'd run after you, kind sir,' she answered me.

Suppose I was too fast for you, my pretty fair maid?
'Then the devil would fetch you back to me, kind sir,' she answered me.

THE SAILOR CUT DOWN

As I was a-walking down by the Royal Albion,
The night it was stormy and so was the day;
When what should I see but one of my shipmates,
Wrapped up in a blanket and colder than clay.

He asked me for a candle to light him to bed with,
Likewise for a flannel to wrap round his head;
His poor head was aching, his sad heart was breaking,
He was a young sailor cut down in his prime.

At the corner of the street all the girls were a-standing,
And one to another they whispered and said:
'There goes the young sailor whose money we've squandered,
There goes the young sailor cut down in his prime.'

O play the drums softly and play the pipe mellowly,
Play the dead march as you carry me on;
Take me to the graveyard and lay the sod over me,
I am a young sailor cut down in my prime.

At the corner of the gravestone these words shall be written,
Come all you young sailors take warning by me;
And don't go out courting the girls of the city,
For the girls of the city was the ruin of me.

SALLY MY DEAR

O Sally, my dear, won't you come to bed to me?
O Sally, my dear, won't you come to bed to me?
She laughs and replies: 'I am sure you'll undo me.'
    Sing whack fol-the-day, ri-fol-the-day,
    Whack fol-the-day.

O Sally, my dear, why should I not undo you?
O Sally, my dear, why should I not undo you?
She laughs and replies: 'You can come to bed to me.'

O Sally, my dear, I can't undo my breeches,
O Sally, my dear, I can't undo my breeches,
She laughs and replies: 'Take a knife, rip the stitches.'

So they undid the stitches and into bed tumbled,
They undid the stitches and into bed tumbled,
I'll leave you to guess how that young couple fumbled.

Now if all those young ladies turned hares on the mountain,
If all those young ladies turned hares on the mountain,
How soon the young men would get guns and go hunting.

And if all those young ladies turned sheep in the clover,
If all those young ladies turned sheep in the clover,
The men would turn rams and they'd ram them all over.

And if all those young ladies turned little red vixen,
And if all those young ladies turned little red vixen,
The men would turn foxes, they chase them and fix 'em.

And if all those young ladies turned fish in deep water,
If all those young ladies turned fish in deep water,
How soon the young men would strip and swim after.

And if all those young ladies turned bells in the tower,
If all those young ladies turned bells in the tower,
The men would turn sextons and bang them each hour.

THE SERGEANT

It was in the green springtime
And Mary lay a-sleeping,
When all of a sudden,
The Sergeant came a-creeping
　　With his whack fol-the-diddle-I-doh
　　And his whack fol-the-diddle-day.

A few months went by
And Mary she grew bolder,
And she wished that the Sergeant
Would come and do her over
　　With his whack fol-the-diddle-I-doh
　　And his whack fol-the-diddle-day.

A few months went by
And Mary she grew fatter,
And all of the neighbours
Began to wonder who'd been at her
    With his whack fol-the-diddle-I-doh
    And his whack fol-the-diddle-day.

A few months went by
And Mary burst asunder,
And out pops a little Sergeant
With a regimental number
    And a whack fol-the-diddle-I-doh
    And a whack fol-the-diddle-day.

A warning, young ladies –
Be sure to keep from under
The spell of a Sergeant,
Or your honour he will plunder
    With his whack fol-the-diddle-I-doh
    And his whack fol-the-diddle-day.

SEVEN NIGHTS DRUNK

The ve-ry first night that I came home, so
drunk I could-n't see, And there was a horse in the
sta-ble where my horse ought to be. So I

102

said to my wife – she's a sweet lit – tle wife – 'Now tell this thing to me, What's that horse in the sta – ble where my horse ought to be?' 'Well,' she says, 'you're drunk you sil –ly old fool, So drunk you can –not see It's no –thing but a milk –ing cow my moth – er sent to me.' Ma – ny miles of the road have I tra –velled, A mill –ion miles or more __ But a sad – dle on a milk – ing –cow I've ne –ver seen be – fore.

The very first night that I came home, so drunk I couldn't see,
And there was a horse in the stable where my horse ought to be.
So I said to my wife - she's a sweet little wife -
'Now tell this thing to me,
What's that horse in the stable where my horse ought to be?'
'Well,' she says, 'you're drunk, you silly old fool,
So drunk you cannot see
It's nothing but a milking cow my mother sent to me.'
Many miles of the road have I travelled,
A million miles or more -
But a saddle on a milking-cow I've never seen before.

Now the very next night that I came home, so drunk I couldn't see,
And there was a coat on the coat-stand where my coat ought to be.
So I said to my wife - she's a sweet little wife -
'Now tell this thing to me,
What's that coat on the coat-stand where my coat ought to be?'
'Well,' she says, 'you're drunk, you silly old fool
So drunk you cannot see
It's nothing but a blanket that my mother sent to me.'
Many miles of the road have I travelled,
A million miles or more -
But buttons on a blanket I have never seen before.

Now the very next night that I came home, so drunk I couldn't see,
And there was a hat on the hat-rack where my hat ought to be.
So I said to my wife - she's a sweet little wife -
'Now tell this thing to me,
What's that hat on the hat-rack where my hat ought to be?'
'Well,' she says, 'you're drunk, you silly old fool,
So drunk you cannot see
It's nothing but a chamber-pot my mother sent to me.'
Many miles of the road have I travelled,
A million miles or more -
But a chamber pot size six and seven-eights I have never seen before.

Now the very next night that I came home, so drunk I couldn't see,
And there was boots under the bed where my boots ought to be.
So I said to my wife - she's a sweet little wife -
'Now tell this thing to me
What's these boots here under the bed where my boots ought to be?'
'Well,' she says, 'you're drunk, you silly old fool,
So drunk you cannot see
It's nothing but two marrows that my mother sent to me.'

Many miles of the road have I travelled,
A million miles or more -
But laces on a marrow I have never seen before.

Now the very next night that I came home, so drunk I couldn't see,
And there was trousers on the bed where my trousers ought to be.
So I said to my wife - she's a sweet little wife -
'Now tell this thing to me,
What's these trousers on the bed where my trousers ought to be?'
'Well,' she says, 'you're drunk, you silly old fool,
So drunk you cannot see
It's nothing but a little flag my mother sent to me.'
Many miles of the road have I travelled,
A million miles or more -
But flies upon the Union Jack I've never seen before.

Now the very next night that I came home, so drunk I couldn't see,
And there was a head on the pillow where my head ought to be.
So I said to my wife - she's a sweet little wife -
'Now tell this thing to me,
What's that head there on the bed where my head ought to be?'
'Well,' she says, 'you're drunk, you silly old fool,
So drunk you cannot see
It's nothing but a baby that my mother sent to me.'
Many miles of the road have I travelled,
A million miles or more -
But a moustache on a baby I have never seen before.

So the very last night that I came home, so drunk I couldn't see,
And there was a thing in my wife's hand where my thing ought to be.
So I said to my wife - she's a sweet little wife -
'Now tell this thing to me,
What's that thing there in your hand where my thing ought to be?'
'Well,' she says, 'you're drunk, you silly old fool,
So drunk you cannot see
It's nothing but a rolling pin my mother sent to me.'
Many miles of the road have I travelled,
A million miles or more -
But b---s upon a rolling pin I have never seen before.

SEVENTEEN COME SUNDAY

As I walked out one May morn-ing, One May morn-ing, so ear-ly; As I walked out one May morn-ing, One May morn-ing so ear-ly, I ov-er-took a hand-some maid Just as the sun was ris-ing. With me roo-rum-rah Fol-the-did-dle-ah Fol-the-didd-le-ay-da-ry-O.

As I walked out one May morning,
One May morning so early;
    As I walked out one May morning,
    One may morning so early,
Just as the sun was rising.
    With me roo-rum-rah
    Fol-the-diddle-ah
    Fol-the-diddle-aye-dary-O.

Her shoes were bright and her stockings white
And her buckles shone like silver;
She had a black and roving eye
And her hair hung over her shoulder.

How old are you, my fair pretty maid?
How old are you, my honey?
She answered me, right modestly:
'I am seventeen come Sunday.'

Will you marry me, my fair pretty maid?
Will you marry me, my honey?
She answered me quite cheerfully:
'I dare not, for my Mammy.

'If you come to my Mammy's house
While the moon is shining brightly
I will come down and let you in
And my Mammy shall not hear me.'

I went to her Mammy's house
While the moon was brightly shining;
She did come down and let me in
And I laid in her arms till the morning.

'Now soldier, will you marry me?
Now is your time or never;
For if you do not marry me,
I am undone for ever.'

And now she is the soldier's wife,
And the soldier loves her dearly;
And the drum and the fife is her delight,
And a merry old man is mine-O.

SEX AND THE SINGLE GIRL

When I came to Town, it got me down, There was
no - one that I knew; Till I met Pete, who was
kind and sweet And told me what to do.

I've tried jump-ing up and down, I've laced my baths with
gin; But it's hard - er far to
get it out Than it was to put it in.

When I came to Town, it got me down,
There was no-one that I knew;
Till I met Pete, who was kind and sweet
And told me what to do.

> I've tried jumping up and down,
> I've laced my baths with gin;
> But it's harder far to get it out
> Than it was to put it in.

Pete never told me of the ring,
The cream or else the cup;
Said: 'Don't take fright, it'll be all right
If you do it standing up.'

So I loved Pete all in the street,
And up against the wall;
He said: 'Just cough when you've had enough
And I swear you'll never fall.'

Now truth to tell, it all went well,
Though I was worried in May;
And got in a state, I was way past the date
And I didn't know what he'd say.

Oh I don't want to get married yet,
I don't want to be a wife;
And I know he'd have thought that he'd been caught
If I'd tied him down for life.

> So I tried jumping up and down,
> And laced my baths with gin;
> But it was harder far to get it out
> Than it was to put it in.

(c) Tony McCarthy, September 1971

THE SHOEMAKER'S KISS

There was an old wom - an who
lived in the West, So green as the
leaves they are green, green, green,
green, So green as the leaves they are green.
She had a young daugh - ter who'd
ne - ver been kissed, And you know ve - ry
well what I mean, mean, mean, mean, You
know ve - ry well what I mean._____

There was an old woman who lived in the West,
    So green as the leaves they are green,
      green, green, green,
    So green as the leaves they are green.
She had a young daughter who'd never been kissed,
    And you know very well what I mean,
      mean, mean, mean,
    You know very well what I mean.

This young girl she rose and she put on her clothes,
And straight to the shoemaker's shop she did go.

Shoemaker, shoemaker, have you got any shoes?
O yes, pretty maiden, I think I'll fit you.

So into the shoemaker's shop she did trip,
And boldly he seized her and kissed her sweet lips.

Six long months being over and past,
This bonny young girl she grew thick round the waist.

Nine long months being over and done,
The bonny young lass had a fine bouncing son.

O daughter, O daughter, how came you by this?
O mother, dear mother, 'twas the shoemaker's kiss.

THE SWEET NIGHTINGALE

My sweetheart come a - long, Don't you hear the sweet song, The sweet song of the night-in-gale flow;___ ___ Don't you hear the fond tale Of the sweet nightin - gale, As he sings in the val - ley be - low ow–ow–ow – ow–ow–ow – ow–ow–ow As he sings in the val - ley be - low.___

My sweetheart come along,
Don't you hear the sweet song,
The sweet song of the nightingale flow;
Don't you hear the fond tale
Of the sweet nightingale
As he sings in the valley below,
        As he sings in the valley below.

Pretty Polly, don't fail,
I shall carry your pail
And along to your cottage we'll go;
We shall hear the fond tale
Of the sweet nightingale
As he sings in the valley below.

Sir, leave me alone,
I have hands of my own
And along with you, sir, I'll not go;
I shan't hear the fond tale
Of the sweet nightingale
As he sings in the valley below.

Now will you agree
To lie here with me
On this bank where the primroses grow;
We shall hear the fond tale
Of the sweet nightingale
As he sings in the valley below.

So this couple agreed
And got to it with speed
And how sweetly the song it did flow;
She's no longer afraid
For to lie in the shade
While he sings in the valley below.

THE TAILOR'S BREECHES

It's of a brisk young tail - or, a sto - ry I'll re - late, He lodged at an inn called the Ram and the Gate; The Ram and the Gate was the place that he did dwell, And wine and wo - men's com - pan - y he loved ex - ceed - ing well. Oh well, Oh well, Oh well, my lads, Oh well, And wine and wo - men's com - pan - y he loved ex - ceed - ing well.

It's of a brisk young tailor, a story I'll relate,
He lodged at an inn called the Ram and the Gate;
The Ram and the Gate was the place that he did dwell,
And wine and women's company he loved exceeding well.

    Oh well, Oh well, Oh well, my lads, Oh well,
      And wine and women's company he loved exceeding well.

Now the tailor he'd been drinking a glass or two of wine,
And not being used for to drink it made his face to shine;
It caused his face to shine, just like the rising sun,
And he swore he'd have a bonny lass before that he went home.

So he took her in his arms and called her his dear honey,
But while they were a-talking, she was fingering of his money;
She was fingering of his money when the tailor smiled and said:
'If you lend me your petticoats, I'll dance like a maid.'

The tailor pulled his breeches off and the petticoats put on,
The tailor danced a dance, and the lassie sang a song;
The tailor danced a dance and they played a pretty tune,
And she danced the tailor's breeches right out of the room.

Oh have you seen a tailor as undone as I'm undone?
My watch and my money and my breeches they are gone;
And now I am undone I'll become a 'garden flower',
And if ever I get my breeches back, I'll never dance no more.

THREE MAIDS A-MILKING

Three maidens a-milking did go,
Three maidens a-milking did go;
And the wind it did blow high,
And the wind it did blow low;
And it toss-ed their pails to and fro,
     Tra-la-la,
       And it tossed their pails to and fro.

They met with a young man they did know,
They met with a young man they did know;
And they said: 'If you've the will,'
And they said: 'If you've the skill,
You can catch us a small bird or two.'

He said: 'You know I have the will,'
And he said: 'You know I have the skill,
And if you will come with me
Down to yonder greenwood tree
We shall catch them by two and by three.'

So they went to the greenwood so free,
So they went to the greenwood so free;
And he beat at the bush,
And his bird it did fly in,
And it flew just above her lily-white knee.

Here's health to the bird in the bush,
Here's health to the very merry doe;
For birds of one feather,
They all do flock together;
Good people say yes or say no,
  Tra-la-la,
   Good people say yes or say no.

THE THRESHING MACHINE

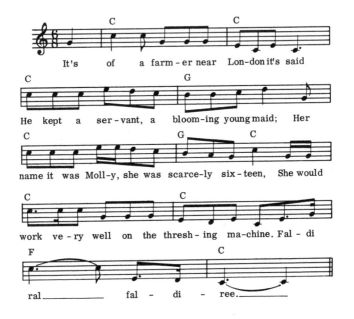

It's of a farmer near London, it's said
He kept a servant, a blooming young maid;
Her name it was Molly, she was scarcely sixteen,
She would work very well on the threshing machine.
    Fal di ral fal di ree.

'O Molly,' said the master, 'the times they are hard,
Will you go with me into the farm yard?
You harness young Dobbin, you know what I mean,
I think we can manage the threshing machine.'

'O Master,' says Molly, 'what will Missus say?'
'Never mind,' says the master, 'she's making of hay,
And while she is spreading the grass that is green
We can be working the threshing machine.'

So the barn doors were open, young Dobbin stood inside,
The farmer got on the machine for to ride;
'O Master,' says Molly, 'your grinding is keen;
I think we can manage the threshing machine.'

Young Dobbin got tired of going round,
He hangs to the traces, he bows to the ground;
Although once in good order, he's now got a wen
Through working so hard at the threshing machine.

O Molly says smiling: 'We now have a loss,
I think it required a much stronger horse;
If Dobbin was strong as before he had been
We'd still keep on working the threshing machine.'

Six months it passed over and, truth for to tell,
Molly's front parlour began for to swell;
And that shortly after she had got her wean
The fruits of her labour with the threshing machine.

THE TROOPER'S HORSE

There was an old wo - man lived
un - der the hill, Fal - a - lo, fal -
lal - a - lal - a - lo, 'If she's not
gone, she lives there still. Fal - a - lo, fal - a -
lo, Fal - la - la - la - la - la - lo.

There was an old woman lived under the hill,
     Fal-a-lo, fal-lal-a-lal-a-lo,
If she's not gone, she lives there still.
     Fal-a-lo, fal-a-lo, fal-la-la-la-la-la-lo.

A jolly dragoon came riding by,
He called for a pot for he was dry.

He called for one drink, then another,
He kissed the daughter, likewise the mother.

The night coming on, the day was spent,
They went to bed with the mother's consent.

O what is this so stiff and warm?
'Tis Bald, my nag, he'll do you no harm.

But what is this? 'Tis a little well
Where Bald your nag may drink his fill.

But what if my nag should chance to fall in?
Take a hold of the grass that grows on the brim.

But what if his hold of the grass should fail?
Throw him in by the mane, pull him out by the tail.

UP FOR THE CUP

I came up to London looking ve - ry swell, All I had was my muff -ler, cap and bell; A lit- tle pot of whis - ky to keep my bo - dy warm, And no thought in me to do a bo - dy harm. I was Up for the Cup, Up for the Cup; Ee - aye - add - i - o, Up for the Cup.

I came up to London looking very swell,
All I had was my muffler, cap and bell;
A little pot of whisky to keep my body warm,
And no thought in me to do a body harm.

    I was Up for the Cup,
    Up for the Cup;
    Ee-aye-addio,
    Up for the Cup.

When the match was over, we had a sup of ale,
And went down to Soho, looking for some tail;
Till a dolly in a doorway, who looked very glum
Said: 'Step inside, warm yourself, and have a bit of fun.'

Well, we stepped inside and we had another sup
Till she says: 'Hey, mister, you'd better pay up';
Till I flashed her the wads that were sticking in my purse
And she says: 'Come to think of it, we'll go to bed first.'

So I rumbled her and tumbled her for all that I was worth
She said: 'Are they all like you Up North?'
I said: 'There are some that are no use at all,
But you can't beat the lads who follow football.'

So I told her of Best and Charlton and Law,
But after half an hour she began to snore;
So I leaped into my trousers and left her a pound,
I'll be back another Saturday for another round.

    I'll be Up for the Cup,
    Up for the Cup;
    Ee-aye-addio,
    Up for the Cup.

© Tony McCarthy

WEARY OF TUMBLING ALONE

One morn - ing of late as I walked in great state I heard a maid - en mak- ing sad moan;_____ I asked her the mat - ter, she said: 'Sir, I won't flat - ter, I am wea - ry of tumb -ling a - lone.'_____

One morning of late as I walked in great state
I heard a maiden making sad moan;
I asked her the matter, she said: 'Sir, I woun't flatter,
I am weary of tumbling alone.'

O that is a pity, that a maiden so pretty
And the young men so idle are grown,
But curse light upon it, and worse may come on it,
If I leave you a-tumbling alone.

'O then,' says the sailor, 'can you fancy me?
I've got gold and got silver in store;
I have brought from the sea such a fine remedy
That will ease you of tumbling alone.'

'O then,' says the fair maid, 'if you can fancy me,
I have got plenty of money in store;
No more cross the main to fight in France or Spain,
Nor go where the loud cannons roar.'

'O then,' says the sailor, 'I can fancy you
As long as your money doth last';
She grows thich in the waist, and thin in the face,
But the sailor he steers off at last.

As down in the garden there grows a red rose
I'll pluck it and call it my own;
In an hour it will fade, and so will a maid
That's weary of tumbling alone.

WHISTLE, DAUGHTER, WHISTLE

Mother, I long to get married, I long to be a bride,
I long to lie by that young man forever at his side;
Forever by his side, O how happy I should be,
For I'm young and merry and almost weary of my virginity.

O daughter, I was twenty before that I was wed,
And many a long and lonesome mile I carried my maidenhead;
O mother, that may be, it's not the case with me,
For I'm young and merry and almost weary of my virginity.

Whistle, daughter, whistle, and you shall have a sheep.
I cannot whistle, mother, but I can sadly weep;
My maidenhead does grieve me that fills my heart with fear,
It's a burden, a heavy burden and more than I can bear.

Whistle, daughter, whistle, and you shall have a cow.
I cannot whistle, mother, indeed I don't know how;
My maidenhead does grieve me that fills my heart with fear,
It's a burden, a heavy burden and more that I can bear.

Whistle, daughter whistle and you shall have a man.
(Whistles): You see very well I can;
You nasty, impudent Jane – what makes you whistle now?
I'd rather whistle for a man than for a sheep or cow.

You nasty, impudent Jane, I'll pull your courage down,
Take off your silks and satins and put on your working gown;
I'll send you to the fields a-tossing of the hay,
With your fork and rake the hay to make and then hear what you say.

Mother, don't be so cruel to send me to the fields,
Where young men may entice me and to them I nay yield;
For, mother, it's well known that I am full well grown
For it is a pity a girl so pretty as I should lay alone.